PROLOGUE: TELLING THE BEES

A CENTURIES-OLD TRADITION IS BASED ON SUPERSTITION.

MANY FAMILIES KEPT BEES BECAUSE THE HIVE PRODUCED HONEY AND REPRESENTED TIGHT FAMILY UNITS THAT WORKED TOGETHER IN HARMONY.

IN PROTEST, THE HIVES REFUSED TO HUM ON THE NEWLY CHRISTENED CHRISTMAS DAY

WHAT DO WE —

QUIETER, PLEASE.

IT IS BELIEVED THAT TELLING THE BEES ENSURES GOOD FORTUNE. NOT TELLING THEM COURTS DISASTER.

SORRY. WHAT... HOW DO WE TELL THEM?

LIKE THIS.

NOK NOK

CELTIC MYTHOLOGY TELLS US THAT BEES ARE MESSENGERS BETWEEN THE WORLD OF THE LIVING AND THE SPIRIT WORLD. THE BEES WERE NOT INFORMED THAT THE GREGORIAN CALENDAR WAS ADOPTED IN ONE TALE.

THE EVENT INSPIRED POET JOHN GREENLEAF WHITTIER TO WRITE "TELLING THE BEES" IN 1858, CANONIZING THE IDEA THAT FAMILY BEES NEEDED TO BE INFORMED WHEN MAJOR LIFE EVENTS AFFECTED THEIR FAMILY.

THE MISTRESS IS DEAD, BUT DON'T YOU GO. YOUR MASTER WILL BE A GOOD MASTER TO YOU

THAT TASK FELL TO 79-YEAR-OLD PALACE BEEKEEPER JOHN CHAPPLE.

HE TOLD THE BEES RESIDING AT
BUCKINGHAM PALACE AND CLARENCE HOUSE
IN HUSHED TONES THAT QUEEN ELIZABETH II
HAD PASSED.

THE MISTRESS IS DEAD,
BUT DON'T YOU GO.
YOUR MASTER WILL BE
A GOOD MASTER TO YOU

AFTER ALL, SHE WAS THE QUEEN
OF QUEENS AND MISTRESS
OF THE HIVES.

GOD SAVE THE QUEEN.

Queen Elizabeth II.

Fifty three countries.

This is the *Commonwealth of Nations* which the Queen heads. It is mostly the former British Empire which transformed itself under her leadership into this Commonwealth as countries were granted independence.

Thirty three of these countries are Republics while five have their own monarchs. The remaining sixteen including Canada, Australia and New Zealand as well as the UK still count the Queen as head of state.

It is often said she is a mere figure head, a person of little influence. As we will see this is a mistaken view. Her influence is much greater than many people recognise or admit — it is subtle but it is definitely there.

She was born *Elizabeth Alexandra Mary* 21 April 1926 by caesarean section at a private house in London's Mayfair.

145 Piccadilly was her early home. Her birth was not a big deal as she was not born to reign.

Her Grandpa was King George V and her dad's older brother was the dashing Prince Edward, the Prince of Wales, the man in line to succeed to the throne.

Surely he would marry and have children and as they in turn had children so Elizabeth would plummet down the line of succession.

She would become it was assumed a minor royal opening smallish hospital wings on wet Wednesdays in distant parts. But, as we will see, it did not turn out like that.

The Archbishop of York baptised Elizabeth in a private crypt in Buckingham Palace on 29 May 1926.

With her younger sister Margaret born in 1930, Elizabeth (or Lilibet as she was called) was educated at home.

Her mother the much adored Queen Elizabeth the Queen Mother and Governess Marion "Crawfie" Crawford oversaw this process.

The 1st Buckingham Palace Company of Girl Scouts is formed so that Elizabeth can mix with girls her own age.

She becomes leader of Swallow Patrol and earns a range of badges from horsewoman and swimmer to cook and needlewoman.

As she turned 10 in 1936 her world changed hugely. Her grandfather King George V dies and her uncle becomes *King Edward VIII*.

However he is in love with a soon-to-be twice divorced American lady called Mrs. Wallis Simpson. He wants to marry her but this creates a huge constitutional crisis.

Bessie Wallis Warfield (1896-1986) was born in Blue Ridge Summit PA and raised in Baltimore MD. She married Earl Spencer Jr. a U.S. navy pilot in 1916, divorcing him in 1927 to marry shipping executive Ernest Simpson in 1928. She was still married when her affair with Edward started the second divorce not coming through until October 1936.

Knowing the Government of Prime Minister Stanley Baldwin would resign if he pressed ahead with marriage plans King Edward VIII abdicates and the new king is George VI; as he is Lilibet's father she is now suddenly first in line to become the next head of state as a Queen.

Edward was never crowned and reigned for only 325 days from 20 Jan to 11 Dec 1936; he does indeed marry Wallis and they lived abroad outside the immediate Royal Family—exiled almost—as Duke and Duchess of Windsor.

...she added wistfully, wondering if there is time for the King and Queen to produce a boy and relieve her of this totally unexpected and unasked for burden. But it was not to be.

King George VI and his wife and daughters set about restoring confidence in the monarchy with a united family image.

And Mrs. Roosevelt comes to visit.

A young minor royal *Prince Philip of Greece and Denmark* drifts in and out of Elizabeth's even younger life.

At age 13 in the summer of 1939 she starts to exchange letters with her future husband.

Like her he is descended directly from Queen Victoria and they are 3rd cousins.

Fall of 1939 sees the outbreak of WWII as Germany invades Poland. Elizabeth and her sister Margaret are moved out of London and west to Windsor Castle.

Replying to a suggestion that the young princesses be evacuated to Canada the King's wife states:

"The children won't go without me I won't leave without the King. And the King will never leave."

Indeed the King famously refused to leave Buckingham Palace in central London while the eastern side of the metropolis was being pounded every night by incoming German bombers.

Elizabeth joins the Women's Auxiliary a branch of the Territorial Army where she learns a range of mechanical skills including how to strip an engine, drive and change a wheel on a truck.

She is the last remaining head of state alive who was in uniform in WWII.

As that war comes to an end so Elizabeth starts to accompany her parents on Royal duties and even goes out solo to official events.

She is very serious about life — her sister Margaret less so!

A huge celebration of the end of war takes place in central London. With parental permission the two young princesses venture out from Buckingham Palace anonymously.

They were terrified of being recognised but linked arms with strangers as hundreds of thousands of people poured down Whitehall from Trafalgar Square to Parliament Square on a tide of euphoria.

Elizabeth wore her Women's Auxiliary uniform. It was actually a pretty good disguise.

On a cold and windy 20 Nov 1947 Elizabeth marries Philip in Westminster Abbey. There was controversy by the bucket-load.

He gave up his titles to become Lieutenant Philip Mountbatten; he had no money; he had not attended the "right" schools; he was a bit arrogant; he was a Greek Orthodox; his sisters' husbands had Nazi connections; and some of Elizabeth's family were deeply opposed and refused to take any part.

But he was made the Duke of Edinburgh and it went ahead beautifully. The Duke and Duchess of Windsor were not invited.

The war had only just ended and this marriage of the young princess and heir to the throne was seen as a major boost to morale.

But rationing was still prevalent and Elizabeth had to save up coupons to purchase the material needed for her gown.

Prince Charles is born in 1948 (for the first time no government officials are guarding the birthplace to ensure the new heir to the throne is not swapped for some other baby) and *Princess Anne* in 1950.

In 1949 the young couple takes up residence in Clarence House near to Buckingham Palace.

Prince Philip is a naval officer still and Elizabeth travels to Malta to spend time with him at his base.

These are very happy days, very happy indeed.

By 1951 the health of the King is very poor. Elizabeth takes on many of his duties including an October 1951 visit to Canada and the USA where she meets President Harry S. Truman the first of many such she is to spend time with both in the USA and the UK.

In early 1952 Elizabeth and Philip set out to visit Australia and New Zealand via Kenya.

They are staying at Sagana Lodge in Kenya when Philip breaks the news to Elizabeth that her father has passed on and that she is now Queen. It is Feb 6th 1952.

The new head of state dressed in black is met at the airport by *Prime Minister Winston Churchill;* he was the first of 12 who have served her to date (2014).

After formalities she drives to be with her mother Elizabeth who now adopts the title "the Queen Mother".

The new Queen and her Consort the Duke of Edinburgh move into Buckingham Palace and begin to plan the Coronation.

Immediately a problem looms. Margaret confides in Elizabeth that she is in love with RAF Group Captain Peter Townsend.

He is a lot older, divorced, not a royal and already a father.

"Wait a year" begs Elizabeth. Margaret obeys and the romance fizzles out.

The Queen's Coronation takes place in Westminster Abbey 2 June 1953. It is a huge magical moment broadcast around the world by radio and TV.

Norman Hartnell who designed her wedding dress now does her Coronation robes incorporating many emblems such as Canada's maple leaf.

Despite inclement weather 500,000 people line the route between the Palace and the Abbey.

Just months after the Coronation Queen Elizabeth and Prince Philip undertake a 6 month tour of the Commonwealth. No King or Queen had ever ventured so far as she went from the Caribbean through the Pacific to Australia and New Zealand. She met thousands of people, gave scores of speeches and was seen by 75% of all Australians.

This trip sets the tone for her whole reign as the British Empire is transformed into the British Commonwealth and finally the Commonwealth of Nations. She travels extensively both in and outside the Commonwealth; she entertains State Visits from many fellow Heads of State including President and Mrs. Obama; and she attends every single meeting of the Commonwealth Heads of Government her health allows. In dealing with the Commonwealth she has no actual constitutional obligation at all to seek the opinion of the British Prime Minister. If and when she does so it is as a courtesy.

Early in 1955 Winston Churchill resigns as Prime Minister. The Queen consults and quickly asks *Sir Antony Eden* to form a government. Later that year Eden comfortably wins a General Election with a majority of 54.

However President Nasser of Egypt seizes the Suez Canal and nationalises the Anglo-French company that operates it. Eden sends in the British Army supported by French and Israeli troops and bombs Egyptian airfields without declaring war. It is said that Queen Elizabeth was opposed. Whatever the truth international pressure and unexpected resistance led to a deeply humiliating ceasefire. A majority of Commonwealth countries votes against the Suez invasion at the UN.

Eden soon resigns on health grounds and, following consultations, the Queen appoints *Harold Macmillan* as her third Prime Minister. Like Churchill he has an American mother.

From afar a young *Margaret Thatcher* is appalled by Eden's approach to Suez and formulates four rules:

Don't go to war unless you are determined to finish it;

Don't go against the policy of the US;

Keep on the right side of international law; and

Never hesitate.

These were to serve her well in the Falkland War and to guide her when she advised the first President Bush on the first Gulf War: "This is no time to go wobbly, George!"

In October 1957 the Queen and Prince Philip celebrate Virginia's 350th anniversary and 500,000+ turn out as she also visits New York City. This trip marks the first of three times she is to meet President Dwight D Eisenhower. Fifty years later they return for Virginia's 400th anniversary! This last visit is her fourth State Visit to the US and she spends time with President and Mrs. George W. Bush in Washington DC.

Back home she meets Marilyn Monroe and Jayne Mansfield.

The Queen's second and third sons, *Prince Andrew* (Duke of York) and *Prince Edward* (Earl of Wessex) are born in 1960 and 1964 and complete her family for the moment — seven grandchildren are to come later.

Sometimes they are called the "spares" in case anything should happen to Charles.

Between their births the Queen and Prince Philip entertain President and Mrs Kennedy in June 1961 at Buckingham Palace. It is said that Jackie upstaged the Queen but the latter is unfazed. The President laughs as Prince Philip is transfixed by Jackie's beauty.

In 1963 Prime Minister Macmillan resigns for health reasons. For the first time the handover of day to day powers is not easy as there are two contenders, *R.A. Butler* and *Alec Douglas Home.* Following soundings the Queen opts for the latter who becomes her 4th Prime Minister. There is uproar in the Conservative Party which now moves to have its MPs elect its future leaders.

A General Election follows and the Queen now has her fifth Prime Minister and her first Socialist one namely *Harold Wilson.* It is said they got on very well indeed, that he adored her and that they both enjoyed their weekly hour long meeting.

To mark the 20th anniversary of the end of WWII the Royal couple undertake a much publicised 10 day tour of West Germany. However they were received very well by huge crowds waving huge banners: "We want you to be our Queen!"

In 1965 she leads the nation in mourning at the State funeral for Winston Churchill and in celebration in 1966 as England wins soccer's World Cup beating West Germany by a score of 4 to 2 in London's Wembley Stadium.

But that fall she struggles to express herself on a visit to Aberfan in Wales where a huge slag heap next to a mine has slipped all the way down a hillside killing 146 people mostly children in the local school.

Relations with the Duke and Duchess of Windsor (the American Mrs. Wallis Simpson) thaw slightly and they are invited to London to see Queen Elizabeth unveil a plaque that commemorates the 100th anniversary of the birth of Queen Mary, the Duke's mother.

1970 sees Harold Wilson surprisingly beaten at the polls and the Queen calls Conservative victor *Edward Heath* to the Palace and asks him to form a government as her sixth Prime Minister. She finds him hard to get along with as he is so pro the European Common Market and so anti her beloved Commonwealth. She is deeply and rightly worried about the Common Market's embargos on trade with Commonwealth countries and the surrender of sovereignty implied in membership of what we now call the EU.

All is happy: Prince Charles is in the Royal Navy; Princess Anne takes the BBC's Sports Personality of the Year Award at age 21 for winning the individual title at the three day horseback European Eventing Championship; Andrew and Edward are growing up and Elizabeth and Philip celebrate their silver wedding anniversary.

But a constitutional crisis looms. The trade unions in particular the National Union of Mineworkers take on Prime Minister Edward Heath who in February 1974 goes to the country asking "Who rules: Government or unions?" The result is inconclusive: Heath wins most votes but Wilson wins most seats! Elizabeth gives the sitting Prime Minister breathing space to try to form a coalition with the Liberal Party but they cannot agree to terms so she turns to Wilson. He goes back to the country and wins a slim but workable majority. Two years later he makes way for "sunny" *Jim Callaghan*, the Queen's seventh Prime Minister and a man who reasons that the Labor Party need not be republican.

In the meantime Margaret Thatcher defeats Heath to become Leader of Her Majesty's Opposition in Parliament. On May 4th 1979 she becomes Queen Elizabeth's eighth and longest serving Prime Minister.

As Britain joins the European Economic Community (now the European Union) so trade with the Commonwealth countries is damaged. Rumblings of discontent are heard but the Queen is a steadying influence despite her deep worries. It is interesting to speculate what would have happened if she had refused to sign the relevant legislation.

The 1970s sees violent attacks on the Royal family. Princess Anne is driving to Buckingham Palace with her first husband when a car veers in front of them and a gunman jumps out. Her driver, bodyguard, a nearby police officer and a passing journalist are all injured or shot before the wannabe kidnapper is overpowered. It is widely thought that this incident inspired the opening of Patriot Games by Tom Clancy where Jack Ryan (played by Harrison Ford) saves the Prince and Princess of Wales and their new son presumably Charles, Diana and William.

Then in the summer of 1979 the IRA kills Lord Mountbatten (known within the Royal family as Uncle Dickie) and two others with a bomb secreted on his pleasure boat.

This is a hard blow as he had been close to the Royal couple and first son Prince Charles. Pictures of the Royal family on the balcony at Buckingham Palace in June 1977 celebrating the Queen's Silver Jubilee show Mountbatten and his nephew Prince Philip together immediately behind the Queen.

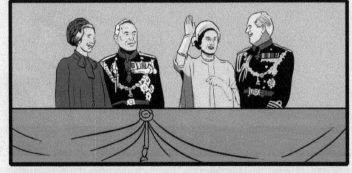

But 1977 had been a true highpoint as the Queen celebrated the Silver Jubilee of her reign – 25 years on the throne. Huge enthusiastic crowds turned out wherever she went. On Jubilee Day – a national holiday – one million people surround Buckingham Palace and line the route her coach takes to St Paul's Cathedral. Not since the end of World War II had the nation celebrated so hard.

The early 1980s sees the Queen slightly eclipsed by two other ladies. In 1980 the Queen Mother turns 80 and the whole country celebrates the life of this much loved icon. A special service is held at St Paul's.

Then the press gets wind of a romance in the life of Prince Charles who is now into his thirties. In February 1981 he becomes engaged to 19-year-old *Lady Diana Spencer*, then a teacher's aide at a kindergarten in Pimlico, central London. She is the daughter of an Earl with no known male skeletons in her cupboard and Charles is under pressure to produce at least one heir and preferably a spare as well.

Charles and Di are interviewed together on TV.

ARE YOU IN *LOVE?*

ERR...

YES OF *COURSE* WE ARE!

WHATEVER "IN LOVE" MEANS.

But July 1982 brings a fairytale wedding. A billion plus people all over the world watch on TV and over 500,000 line the route. Lady Diana — now Princess Diana — is hugely, alarmingly to some, popular. She was never to "bond" with Elizabeth and she found the media to be terribly intrusive.

A year earlier in June 1981 sees a moment of high drama. En route to the annual ceremony of Trooping the Colour the Queen is riding her horse Burmese side-saddle. It is about half a mile from Buckingham Palace to Horse Guards Parade — east down the Mall, turn right and it is on the left. You cannot miss it. Suddenly a man fires six shots at the Queen but fortunately he is using a starting pistol. Burmese is startled but the Queen controls him and both are safe.

It is an eventful start
to the decade:

Prince Andrew is off at war in the
Falkland Islands flying helicopters
off of HMS Invincible;

Lady Diana produces her first
son *William* who will one day
become King — thank goodness
he looks more like his mom than
his dad; and

An intruder scales the walls of
Buckingham Palace, climbs in a
window, wanders around for
30 minutes, finds the Queen's
bedroom and wakes her as he
sits down on the end of the bed
and starts to chat. It takes a long
while before a servant realises
something is wrong and he is
apprehended; a major security
review follows.

While Lady Diana produces a second
son *Prince Henry* (to be always
called Harry) it is clear to all that
the marriage is all but over.

Princess Anne's marriage to
Capt. Mark Phillips is also on the
rocks and she eventually remarries
Royal Equerry Commander (later
Vice Admiral) Timothy Laurence.

While Prince Andrew marries the
bubbly outspoken Sarah Ferguson
who quickly produces Princess
Beatrice and Princess Eugenie,
the marriage of the Duke and
Duchess of York as they are
now known is soon on the rocks.

And Prince Edward is struggling to
find a role for himself so it is all
becoming a bit of a farce.

It all comes to a head in 1992 the year the Queen calls my "annus horribilis" or horrible year:

- Prince Charles separates
- Prince Andrew separates
- Princess Anne divorces
- Duchess of York pictured topless
- Phone calls between Charles and an ex-girlfriend intercepted, taped and leaked
- Ditto Lady Diana and a male friend and...
- Windsor Castle catches fire and burns for hours.

To woo public opinion the Queen starts to pay income tax and opens up Buckingham Palace to the public; the entrance fees go to fix the fire damage at Windsor. Charles makes a movie of his life and work. It is broadcast while his mother the Queen visits with President Yeltsin in Russia and it overshadows this historic moment as Charles admits to adultery on prime time TV.

Margaret Thatcher has been replaced by the grey-faced *John Major* as the Queen's ninth Prime Minister. All of her eight former Prime Ministers were older than Elizabeth, some by decades such as Churchill and some by only months as in Thatcher. Major is the first to be younger. He loses to New Labour's Tony Blair in 1997 and Tony becomes her tenth Prime Minister.

Tony brightly: "Your Majesty, please call me Tony."

Queen Elizabeth pointedly: "I think not, Prime Minister."

What a regal put down but he always gushed all over her.

While the Queen visits South Africa to spend time with President Nelson Mandela, Lady Diana is secretly being filmed by the BBC. Her marriage had always been "crowded" she says in an obvious dig at Camilla Parker-Bowles. Diana wonders aloud if Charles is fit to be King and she too admits adultery. Maybe Charles should be bypassed with the throne going straight to her first son William.

With her first three children now divorced the Queen yearned for quieter times on the family front but it was not to be. In late August 1997 she is woken up in the early hours at Balmoral, her Scottish castle. The news is truly shocking. There has been a terrible car crash in Paris. Lady Diana, her new lover Dodi Fayed and their driver are all dead — only Diana's bodyguard has survived and only just.

Prince Charles and sons William and Harry are staying with the Queen at Balmoral. The two boys are desperately upset at losing their much loved Mom. The Prince and the Queen make a strategic decision to stay in Scotland to shield the grieving boys from the media. It is a well intentioned idea but it backfires massively.

The Queen and Prince Charles had completely misjudged the level of popularity enjoyed by Lady Diana. Within hours of her death people were camping outside of Westminster Abbey to get the best view of the funeral which would be at least five or six days hence. Thousands and thousands of bouquets piled up and press coverage was 24 hours a day wall to wall.

As the week went by criticism of the lack of any message or emotion on the part of the Queen or her elder son and heir moved from a trickle to a tsunami. Suddenly Palace officials changed tack. Queen Elizabeth returned to London; the flag over Buckingham Palace now flew at half mast; the Monarch and her Consort Prince Philip walked among the banked walls of flowers reading the messages on them; as Queen and grandmother she broadcasts her grief to the nation; and the route Diana's funeral cortege would take was lengthened to accommodate all those wishing to pay respects.

All over the world a billion plus people watch Diana's final journey.

2002, the Queen's Golden Jubilee year, started badly with the death of her sister Margaret. However the Queen presses on with official visits to Jamaica, Australia and New Zealand.
She is barely back when her Mom aged nearly 102 passes on.
One million people line the route her cortege takes to Westminster Abbey. The level of affection for this great icon surprises the media and the Palace.

The Queen and Prince Philip spend May criss-crossing the UK visiting scores of towns and cities. In early June there is a special four day Jubilee weekend which is a huge success by any measure. It ends with millions of people filling the parks around Buckingham Palace as an armada of planes flies in symbolically from the East End of London — which took the brunt of the bombing in WWII — and heads down the Mall and over the Palace. Last of all come a Concorde in formation with the Red Arrows (the Royal Air Force's display team) as Queen Elizabeth waves from the Palace balcony.

Returning from a tour of Canada the Queen feels the Monarchy or the "firm" as she calls it is riding high. However Lady Diana's former butler goes on trial accused of stealing hundreds of items from her and her family. Several days into the trial the Queen comments to Prince Charles that five years earlier the butler had told her that he was keeping lots of things safely stored.

Prince Charles realizes in a blink the importance of this revelation and sends a note to the judge. The trial collapses and the anti-monarchists have a field day.

Prince Charles starts appearing more and more in public with Camilla Parker-Bowles and slowly but surely the public begins to accept his love for her. They marry in April 2005.

In 2007 after a decade in Downing Street (nearly as long as Margaret Thatcher) Tony Blair makes way for the Queen's eleventh Prime Minister namely *Gordon Brown*. Her twelfth soon followed in May 2010 when *David Cameron* headed up a Coalition Government.

Through her weekly meetings with twelve Prime Ministers, her countless visits with heads of state both at home and abroad, her leadership of the Commonwealth of Nations and her daily study of the constant flow of Red Boxes containing official documents Her Majesty is surely one of the most knowledgeable experts on politics and international affairs in the world.

She has a deep sense of patriotism and duty and has never faltered. All 12 of her Prime Ministers (even the grumpy Ted Heath) are on record as deeply appreciating her advice.

She has always been passionate about the Commonwealth of Nations and is deeply respected in all member countries.

Of the 12 US Presidents from Harry S. Truman to Barack Obama she spends serious time with all of them with just one exception namely Lyndon B Johnson. She would have met him at President Kennedy's funeral but she was too pregnant to travel. He in turn was then too busy with the Vietnam War to visit her. She became particularly close with President Ronald Reagan with whom she shared a love of horses. He was the only US President to visit with her and indeed stay at Windsor Castle and the following year she and Prince Philip visited Reagan's California ranch. She was also close with the Bush family as George H. W. Bush welcomed her on her 3rd official State Visit and his son George W. Bush on her 4th; the latter also visited her twice in the UK.

While she is happiest with her dogs and horses, going to the races, photography and country pursuits she also surfs the web, emails, and has a mobile phone and iPod.

She has faced down Australian republicanism and French separatism in Quebec, Canada. She has welcomed post-apartheid South Africa back into the Commonwealth and she has worked with Margaret Thatcher and Tony Blair to bring peace to Northern Ireland.

At a time of great change she has been a pillar of stability.

EPILOGUE: LONG MAY HE REIGN

ON SEPTEMBER 8, 2022, ELIZABETH II DIED AT BALMORAL CASTLE IN SCOTLAND. AT 96, SHE WAS THE LONGEST-LIVING AND LONGEST-REIGNING BRITISH MONARCH.

KING CHARLES III AND THE QUEEN CONSORT WERE AT BALMORAL.

WITHIN HALF AN HOUR OF HER PASSING, PRINCE WILLIAM, PRINCE ANDREW, PRINCE EDWARD, AND THE COUNTESS OF WESSEX ARRIVED

THE ROYAL FAMILY ANNOUNCED HER DEATH ON TWITTER:

THE QUEEN DIED PEACEFULLY AT BALMORAL THIS AFTERNOON. THE KING AND THE QUEEN CONSORT WILL REMAIN AT BALMORAL THIS EVENING AND WILL RETURN TO LONDON TOMORROW.

HER DEATH SET IN MOTION OPERATION LONDON BRIDGE -- ESSENTIALLY HER FUNERAL ARRANGEMENTS, MUCH OF WHICH SHE PLANNED HERSELF.

A SET OF PROTOCOLS SURROUNDING THE QUEEN'S DEATH, OPERATION UNICORN, WAS ALSO ACTIVATED.

THE DEATH OF MY BELOVED MOTHER, HER MAJESTY THE QUEEN, IS A MOMENT OF THE GREATEST SADNESS FOR ME AND ALL MEMBERS OF MY FAMILY.

WE MOURN PROFOUNDLY THE PASSING OF A CHERISHED SOVEREIGN AND A MUCH-LOVED MOTHER. I KNOW HER LOSS WILL BE DEEPLY FELT THROUGHOUT THE COUNTRY, THE REALMS, AND THE COMMONWEALTH, AND BY COUNTLESS PEOPLE AROUND THE WORLD.

ON MONDAY, SEPTEMBER 19, THE QUEEN'S FUNERAL WAS HELD AT WESTMINSTER ABBEY AT 11 A.M.

AT 11:55 A.M., THE LAST POST SOUNDED, AND A NATIONWIDE TWO-MINUTE SILENCE WAS OBSERVED.

FOLLOWING THE STATE FUNERAL, HER COFFIN, FOLLOWED BY KING CHARLES III AND MEMBERS OF THE ROYAL FAMILY, MADE ITS WAY TO ST. GEORGE'S CHAPEL ON THE GROUNDS OF WINDSOR CASTLE, AND HER COFFIN WAS LOWERED INTO THE ROYAL VAULT BELOW THE CHAPEL.

SHE JOINS HER SISTER, PRINCESS MARGARET, AND HER LATE HUSBAND, PRINCE PHILLIP.

GOD SAVE THE QUEEN

TIDALWAVE
COMICS

John Blundell & Michael L. Frizell — Writer

Pablo Martinena, Luciano Kars & Ernesto Lovera — Art

Pablo Martinena & Gary Scott Beatty — Letters

Darren G. Davis — Editor

Pablo Martinena — Cover

Cover B: Azim

Darren G. Davis
Publisher

Maggie Jessup
Publicity

Susan Ferris
Entertainment Manager

Steven Diggs Jr.
Marketing Manager

CPSIA information can be obtained
at www.ICGtesting.com
Printed in the USA
LVHW061930071022
730037LV00040B/176